THE LOOK OF L

the classic s[ongs of]

chappell
£10.99

Burt Bacharach

WISE PUBLICATIONS
LONDON / NEW YORK / SYDNEY / PARIS / COPENHAGEN / MADRID

INTERNATIONAL MUSIC PUBLICATIONS LIMITED
SOUTHEND ROAD, WOODFORD GREEN, ESSEX IG8 8HN, ENGLAND

Dionne Warwick

Dusty Springfield

The Walker Brothers

Sandie Shaw

Gene Pitney

Aretha Franklin

Jackie DeShannon

Billy J Kramer

The Shirelles

Bobby Vinton

Bobby Gentry

Cilla Black

B J Thomas

The Carpenters

The Stylistics

Neil Diamond

Christopher Cross

DIONNE WARWICK
Walk On By

Music by Burt Bacharach. Words by Hal David.

gave me   when you said good - bye - - - eye - - eye -

eye, _____ so walk on   by. ____   So walk on   by, ___

____   you walk on   by. _____

So walk on ____   by, _____

I Just Don't Know
What To Do With Myself

Words by Hal David. Music by Burt Bacharach.

Medium slow

1. I just don't know what to do with my - self.
(Verse 2 see block lyric)
Don't know just what to do with my - self. I'm so used to do - ing

Verse 2:
I just don't now what to do with my time,
I'm so lonesome for you it's a crime.
Going to a movie only makes me sad,
Parties make me feel as bad.
When I'm not with you,
I just don't know what to do.

Make It Easy On Yourself

Music by Burt Bacharach. Words by Hal David.

Oh,_____ break-ing up_____ is

so_____ ve-ry hard_____ to do.

Verse 2:
And if the way I hold you
Can compare to his caress,
No words of consolation
Will make me miss you less.
My darling, if this is goodbye,
I just know I'm gonna cry;
So run to him before you start crying too.

And make it easy…

(There's) Always Something There To Remind Me

Words by Hal David. Music by Burt Bacharach.

Bossa Nova

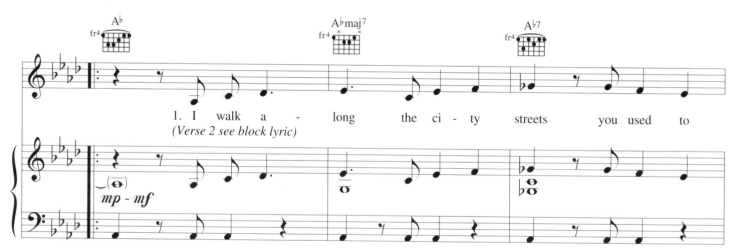

1. I walk a - long the ci - ty streets you used to
(Verse 2 see block lyric)

walk a - long— with me;— And ev - 'ry

Verse 2:
When shadows fall, I pass a small cafe
Where we would dance at night.
And I can't help recalling how it felt
To kiss and hold you tight.

Oh, how can I forget you…

GENE PITNEY

Twenty Four Hours From Tulsa

Words & Music by Burt Bacharach & Hal David.

D.%. al Coda   **⊕ Coda**

ARETHA FRANKLIN

I Say A Little Prayer

Words by Hal David. Music by Burt Bacharach.

1. The mo-ment I wake up,
(Verse 2 see block lyric)

be-fore I put on my make-up, I say a lit-tle prayer for you.

ev - er and ev - er we nev - er will part,_____ oh

how I'll love you, to - geth - er, to - geth - er, that's

how it must be.____ To live with - out you would

1. Smoothly

on - ly mean heart - break for me.____

2. Smoothly

me. My dar - ling be -

lieve me, for me there is no one but you. Please love me

too. I'm in love with

Verse 2:
I run for the bus, dear;
While riding, I think of us dear.
I say a little prayer for you.
At work I just take time,
And all through my coffee break time
I say a little prayer for you.

Forever, forever, *etc.*

What The World Needs Now Is Love

Words by Hal David. Music by Burt Bacharach.

What the world needs now is love, sweet love.

It's the on-ly thing____ that there's just____ too lit-tle of.____ What the

Verse 2:
Lord, we don't need another meadow,
There are cornfields and wheatfields enough to grow.
There are sunbeams and moonbeams enough to shine.
Oh listen, Lord, if you want to know.

Trains And Boats And Planes

Music by Burt Bacharach. Words by Hal David.

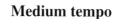

Medium tempo

Trains and boats and planes were pass-ing by; they mean a trip

to Pa - ris or Rome to some-one else, but not for me.

The trains and the boats and planes took you a -

way, a - way from me.

We were so in love, and high a - bove we had a star

DIONNE WARWICK
Anyone Who Had A Heart
Words by Hal David, Music by Burt Bacharach.

take me _____ in his arms and _____ love me too. You could-n't real-ly have a heart and hurt me _____ like you hurt me and be so un-true. What am I to do?_____ Ev-'ry time you go a-way, _____ I al-ways say_____

44

love me, Why won't you?＿＿＿＿ An-y-one who had a heart would love me

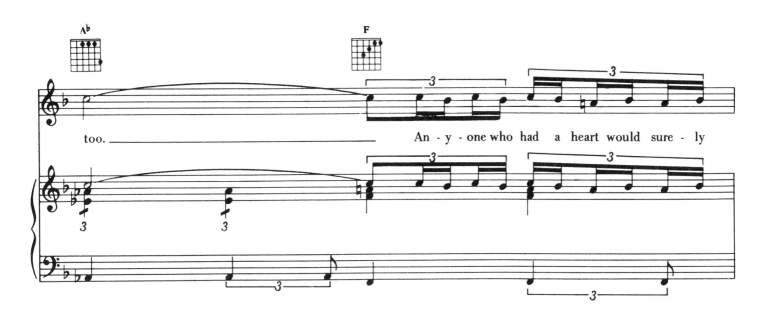

too.＿＿＿＿＿＿＿ An-y-one who had a heart would sure-ly

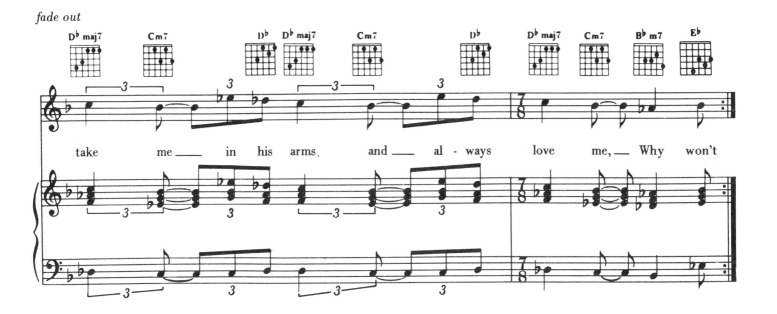

fade out

take me ＿ in his arms ＿ and ＿ al-ways love me, ＿ Why won't

Baby, It's You

Words & Music by Mack David, Burt Bacharach & Barney Williams.

Medium tempo

(Sha la la la la) (Sha la la la

la) (Sha la la la la) (Sha la la la

la) 1. It's not the way you smile that touched my heart.
(Verse 2 see block lyric)

50

Verse 2:
You should hear what they say about you:
(Cheat, cheat)
They say you've never been true.
(Cheat, cheat)
Doesn't matter what they say,
I know I'm gonna love you any old way.
What can I do, when it's true
I don't want nobody? Baby, it's you.

BOBBY VINTON

Blue On Blue

Music by Burt Bacharach. Words by Hal David.

Medium tempo

Blue on blue, heart-ache on heart-ache; blue on blue,

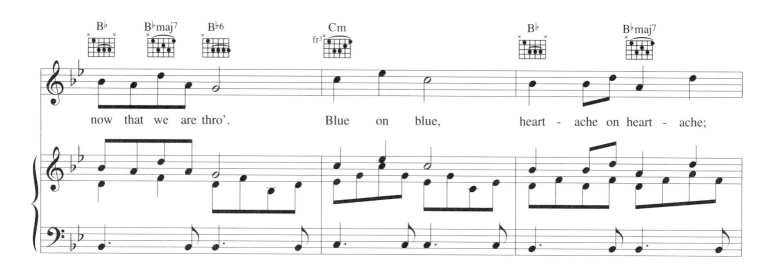

now that we are thro'. Blue on blue, heart-ache on heart-ache;

and I find I can't_____ get ov-er los-ing you. I walk a-

To Coda

D.C. al Coda

53

DUSTY SPRINGFIELD
The Look Of Love
Words by Hal David. Music by Burt Bacharach.

Medium rock ballad

Verse 2:

You've got the look of love, it's on your face,
A look that time can't erase.
Be mine tonight, let this be just the start
Of so many nights like this;
Let's take a lover's vow
And then seal it with a kiss.

I can hardly wait *etc.*

Verse 3: (Instrumental)

I can hardly wait *etc.*

DIONNE WARWICK

Do You Know The Way
To San Jose

Words by Hal David. Music by Burt Bacharach.

Moderato

1. Do you know the way to San Jo se? I've been a way so

(Verse 2 see block lyric)

long, I may go wrong and lose my way. Do you know the

Weeks turn in - to years, how quick they pass, and all the stars

that ne - ver were are park - ing cars and pump - ing gas.

1. **2.**

I've got lots of

friends in San Jo - se.

Do you know the way to San— Jo - se?

are park - ing cars and pump - ing gas.

I've got lots of friends in San Jo - se.

Do you know the way to San Jo - se?

Can't wait to get back to San Jo - se.

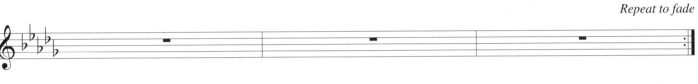

Verse 2:
You can really breathe in San Jose.
They've got a lot of space,
There'll be a place where I can stay.
I was born and raised in San Jose.
I'm going back to find
Some peace of mind in San Jose.
Fame and fortune is a magnet,
It can pull you far away from home.
With a dream in your heart, you're never alone.
Dreams turn into dust and blow away;
And there you are without a friend,
You pack your car and ride away.

I'll Never Fall In Love Again

Words by Hal David. Music by Burt Bacharach.

1. What do you get when you fall in love?
(Verses 2 & 3 see block lyric)

guy with a pin to burst your bub - ble: that's what you get for

Verse 2:
What do you get when you kiss a guy?
You get enough germs to catch pneumonia.
After you do, he'll never phone ya.
I'll never fall in love again,
I'll never fall in love again.

Verse 3:
What do you get when you fall in love?
You only get lies and pain and sorrow.
So, for at least until tomorrow,
I'll never fall in love again,
I'll never fall in love again.

Gene Pitney

True Love Never Runs Smooth

Music by Burt Bacharach. Words by Hal David.

Verse 2:

When the world outside my arms is pulling us apart,
Press your lips to mine and hold me with your heart.
For true love never runs smooth:
That's what they say, but
True love is worth all the pain,
The heartaches and tears we have to pay.

CILLA BLACK

Alfie

Music by Burt Bacharach. Words by Hal David.

Very slowly, rubato

B J THOMAS
Raindrops Keep Falling On My Head
Words by Hal David. Music by Burt Bacharach.

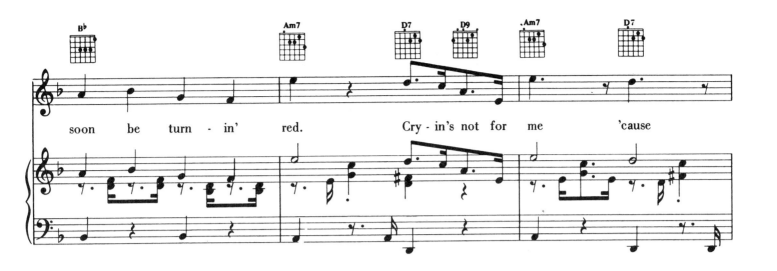

soon be turn-in' red. Cry-in's not for me 'cause

I'm nev-er gon-na stop the rain by com-plain-in'. Be - cause I'm

free noth-in's wor-ry-in' me.

(They Long to Be)
Close To You

Words by Hal David. Music by Burt Bacharach.

Moderato

1. Why do birds sud-den-ly ap-pear
(Verse 2 see block lyric)
ev-'ry

time you are near? Just like me,

On the day that you were born the an-gels got to-ge-ther,___ and de-ci-ded to cre-ate a dream come true. So they sprink-led moon-dust in your hair___ of

Verse 2:
That is why all the girls in town
Follow you all around.
Just like me, they long to be
Close to you.

Wishin' And Hopin'

Words by Hal David. Music by Burt Bacharach.

you won't get him think-in' and a-pray-in',___ wish-in' and a-hop-in'.___ 'Cos

wish-in' and hop-in' and think-in' and pray-in', plan-nin' and dream-in' his

kis - ses will start:_____ that won't get you in - to his heart.___

N.C. So if you're think-in' a-how great true love is,_____

90

Coda is marked **To Coda ⊕** and **D.%. al Coda** with **⊕ Coda**.

all you got-ta do — is hold him and kiss him and squeeze him and love him, just

do it and af-ter you do, you — will be his. You got-ta show him that you

his. You will be his.

molto rit.

You will be his.

THE STYLISTICS

You'll Never Get To Heaven
(If You Break My Heart)

Music by Burt Bacharach. Words by Hal David.

Moderato

1. Mo-ther told me al-ways to fol-low the gold-en rule,
(Verse 2 see block lyric)

Lyrics:
If you break my____ heart,____
break my____ heart.____
I can hard-ly wait for the day when we say "I do."
It's the day I've dreamed of so long, now it's com-ing true.

Verse 2:
I've been hearing rumours about how you play around.
Tho' I don't believe what I hear, still it gets me down.
If you ever should say goodbye,
It would be so awful the angels would cry.

You'll never get to heaven …

Dionne Warwick
Promises, Promises

Music by Burt Bacharach. Words by Hal David.

Medium fast

1. Pro - mi - ses, pro - mi - ses: some are through with pro - mi - ses, pro - mi - ses now. I don't know

(Verse 2 see block lyric)

how I got the nerve_____ to walk

out._____ If I shout,_____ re - mem - ber_____ I feel

free._____ Now I can look at my - self_____ and be

proud;_____ I'm laugh - ing out loud.

Oh, Oh, pro - mi - ses, their kind of pro - mi - ses, can just des -

Verse 2:
Promises, promises: this is where those
Promises, promises end.
I won't pretend that was wrong can be right.
Every night I sleep now,
No more lies.
Things that I promised myself fell apart,
But I found my heart.

NEIL DIAMOND
Heartlight

Words & Music by Carole Bayer Sager, Burt Bacharach & Neil Diamond.

Medium tempo

Come back a - gain,

1. I want you to stay next time.

all the world to see. Turn on your heart-light in the mid-dle of a young boy's dream. Don't wake me up too soon: gon-na take a ride a-cross the moon, you and me.

To Coda

Verse 2:
He's looking for home;
'Cos everyone needs a place,
And home's the most excellent place of all.
And I'll be right here if you should call me.

Turn on your heartlight, *etc.*

Verse 3:
And home's the most excellent place of all.
And I'll be right here if you should call me.

Turn on your heartlight, *etc.*

Arthur's Theme
(Best That You Can Do)

Words & Music by Burt Bacharach, Carole Bayer Sager,
Christopher Cross & Peter Allen.

Moderately

Once in your life you'll find_____ her,
Ar - thur, he does what he plea - ses.

If you get caught be-tween the moon and New York Ci - - - - ty, the best that you can do, the best that you can do is fall— in love.—

Distributors:
Music Sales Limited
8/9 Frith Street, London W1V 5TZ, England.
Music Sales Pty Limited
120 Rothschild Avenue, Rosebery, NSW 2018, Australia.
Order No.AM937475
ISBN 0-7119-5804-1
Visit the Internet Music Shop at
http://www.musicsales.co.uk

International Music Publications Limited
Southend Road, Woodford Green, Essex IG8 8HN, England.
International Music Publications Limited
25 Rue D'Hauteville, 75010 Paris, France.
International Music Publications Gmbh, Germany
Marstallstrasse 8, D-80539 Munchen.
Order Ref. 4195 A
ISBN 1-85909-384-1

New music arrangements by Roger Day.
New music processing by Paul Ewers Music Design.
Book design by Michael Bell Design.
Cover photograph courtesy of The Image Bank.
Text photographs courtesy of
Harry Goodwin, Pictorial Press and Barry Plummer.

Printed in the United Kingdom by
Redwood Books Limited, Trowbridge, Wiltshire.